To Deanne - Christmas 1963
from Mom and Dad

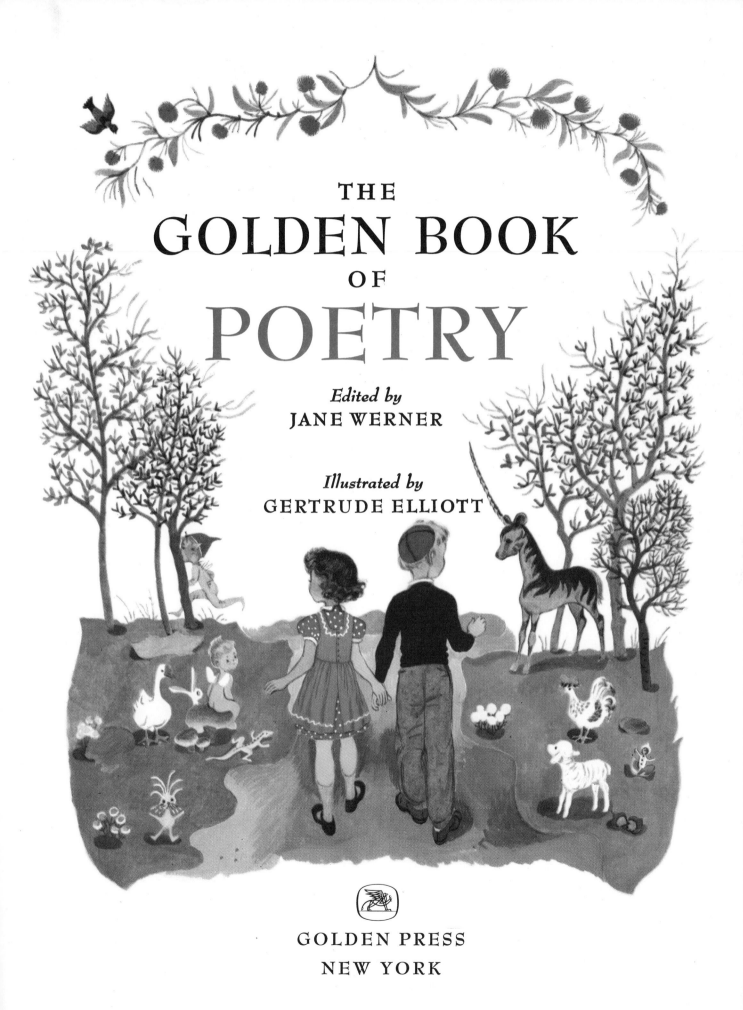

THE
GOLDEN BOOK
OF
POETRY

Edited by
JANE WERNER

Illustrated by
GERTRUDE ELLIOTT

GOLDEN PRESS

NEW YORK

CONTENTS

Fourteenth Printing, 1963

ACKNOWLEDGMENTS

D. Appleton-Century Co.: "The Little Elf" from *The Foothills of Parnassus* by John Kendrick Bangs and from *St. Nicholas Magazine*, copyright 1893 by The Century Co., 1941 by D. Appleton-Century Co.; and "The Elf and the Dormouse" from *Artful Antiks* by Oliver Herford, copyright 1894 by The Century Co., 1922 by Oliver Herford. Mildred Bowers Armstrong: "Boredom" and "Spring Signs" from *Child Life*. Basil Blackwell: "What the Toys Are Thinking" and "Choosing Shoes" by Ffrida Wolfe. The Bobbs-Merrill Co.: "Extremes" from *The Book of Joyous Children* and "The Raggedy Man" and "Little Orphant Annie" from *Rhymes of Childhood*, both by James Whitcomb Riley. Alice B. Campbell: "Sally and Manda" from *Child Life*. Marchette Gaylord Chute: "The Secret" and "Growing Up" from *Child Life*. Curtis Brown, Ltd.: "Jonathan Bing Dances for Spring" from *Jonathan Bing and Other Verses*, copyright 1936 by Beatrice Curtis Brown, by permission of the author. Doubleday and Co.: "General Store," "Animal Store," and "Taxis" from *Taxis and Toadstools* by Rachel Field, copyright 1926 by Doubleday, Doran and Co.; "The Best Game the Fairies Play" and "Differences" from *Fairies and Chimneys* by Rose Fyleman, copyright 1920 by Doubleday, Doran and Co.; "Mice" and "The Little Shepherdess" from *Fifty-one New Nursery Rhymes* by Rose Fyleman, copyright 1932 by Doubleday, Doran and Co. Gerald Duckworth and Co., Ltd.: "The Frog" from *The Bad Child's Book of Beasts* by Hilaire Belloc. Richard W. Emery: "Billy Goats Chew" from *Child Life*. Aileen Fisher: "Otherwise" from *Child Life*. Rose Fyleman, Messrs. Methuen, and The Society of Authors: the poems of Rose Fyleman cited above in the acknowledgment to Doubleday and Co. Harcourt, Brace and Co.: "The Bear Hunt" from *Little Boy and Girl Land* by Margaret Widdemer, copyright 1924 by Harcourt, Brace and Co. Henry Holt and Co.: "The Cupboard," "Miss T.," and "Some One" from *Peacock Pie* by Walter de la Mare. Houghton Mifflin Co.: "The Camel's Complaint" from *The Admiral's Caravan* by Charles Edward Carryl, "The Sea Shell" from *A Dome of Many-colored Glass* by

Amy Lowell, and "Daisies" from *Littlefolk Lyrics* by Frank Dempster Sherman. Florence Page Jaques: "A Goblinade" and "There Was Once a Puffin" from *Child Life*. Alfred A. Knopf, Inc.: "The Frog" from *The Bad Child's Book of Beasts* by Hilaire Belloc. J. B. Lippincott Co.: "Mouse" from *Poems by a Little Girl* by Hilda Conkling and "Jill Came From the Fair" from *Over the Garden Wall* by Eleanor Farjeon. Little, Brown and Co.: "The Tale of Custard, the Dragon" from *The Face Is Familiar* by Ogden Nash and "The Baby Goes to Boston" from *Tirra Lirra* by Laura E. Richards. Lothrop, Lee and Shepard Co.: "Who Likes the Rain?" from *Child Lore* by Clara Doty Bates. The Macmillan Co.: "Color" and "Who Has Seen the Wind?" from *Sing Song* by Christina G. Rossetti; "The Little Turtle" from *Collected Poems* by Vachel Lindsay; and "Gypsies" from *The Pointed People* by Rachel Field. Robert McBride and Co.: "A Bug" and "Tea Party" from *The Coffee-pot Face* by Aileen Fisher. Mildred Plew Meigs Estate: "If I Were a One-legged Pirate," "Moon Song," and "The Road to Raffydiddle" by Milded Plew Meigs. G. P. Putnam's Sons: "Radiator Lions" from *Everything and Anything*, copyright 1925, 1926, 1927, by Dorothy Aldis; "The Ice Man" from *Hop, Skip, and Jump* and "For Christmas" from *Here, There, and Everywhere*, both by Dorothy Aldis. Charles Scribner's Sons: "Wynken, Blynken, and Nod" from *With Trumpet and Drum*, and "The Duel" and "The Sugar-plum Tree" from *A Little Book of Western Verse*, both by Eugene Field. Frederick Warne and Co.: "The Owl and the Pussy-cat" from *The Nonsense Book* by Edward Lear. The Viking Press: "Firefly," "The Picnic," "The People," "Water Noises," and "The Woodpecker" from *Under the Tree* by Elizabeth Madox Roberts, copyright 1922, 1930, by The Viking Press, Inc. Dixie Willson: "Mr. Rabbit" from *Child Life*. Yale University Press: "Serious Omission" from *Songs for Parents* by John Farrar.

The publishers have made a diligent but unsuccessful effort to locate the copyright owners of several other poems in this book.

IF I WERE A ONE-LEGGED PIRATE

MILDRED PLEW MEIGS

If I were a one-legged pirate
　Ga-lumping around on a peg,
I'd flourish my pistol and fire it;
　Then, sure as my right wooden leg,
I'd buy me a three-decker galleon
　With cannon to port and to lee,
And wearing the king's medallion,
　I'd head for a tropical sea!
Roaring a rough Ha-ha! Ha-ho!
　Roving the routes of old,
Over the billows we would go
　Sweeping the seas for gold!
　　Plying the lane
　　Of the Spanish Main
　　　For Gold!
　　　　Gold!
　　　　　Gold!

If I were a one-legged pirate
　Ga-lumping around after loot,
I'd flourish my pistol and fire it;
　Then, sure as my red leather boot,
I'd buy me a three-decker galleon
　With cannon to thunder a mile,
And bucking the sea like a stallion,
　I'd head for a tropical isle!
Roaring a rough Ha-ha! Ha-ho!
　Chanting a chantey bold,
Over the billows we would blow,
　Sweeping the seas for gold!
　　Plying the lane
　　Of the Spanish Main
　　　For Gold!
　　　　Gold!
　　　　　Gold!

But since I was not born a pirate
　Ga-lumping around on a stick;
And since my toy gun when I fire it
　Gives out but a little toy click;
Pretending my boat is a galleon,
　My pond is a tropical sea,
I'll play I'm an old rapscallion,
　But really I won't hurt a flea.
Roaring my small Ha-ha! Ha-ho!
　Saying I'm someone bold,
Over the duck pond I will go
　Roving the routes of old;
　　Plying the pond
　　And the stream beyond
　　　For Gold!
　　　　Gold!
　　　　　Gold!

JILL CAME FROM THE FAIR*
ELEANOR FARJEON

Jill came from the Fair
With her pennies all spent;
She had had her full share
Of delight and content;
She had ridden the ring
To a wonderful tune,
She had flown in a swing
Half as high as the moon,

In a boat that was drawn
By an ivory swan
Beside a green lawn
On a lake she had gone,
She had bought a gold packet
That held her desire;
She had touched the red jacket
Of one who ate fire,

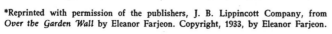

*Reprinted with permission of the publishers, J. B. Lippincott Company, from *Over the Garden Wall* by Eleanor Farjeon. Copyright, 1933, by Eleanor Farjeon.

She had stood at the butt,
And although she was small
She had won a rough nut
With the throw of a ball,
And across the broad back
Of a donkey a-straddle,
She had jolted like Jack-
In-the-Box on a saddle—

Till mid frolic and shout
And tinsel and litter,
The lights started out
Making everything glitter,
And dazed by the noise
And the blare and the flare,
With her toys and her joys
Jill came from the Fair.

A GOBLINADE

FLORENCE PAGE JAQUES

A green hobgoblin,
  Small but quick,
Went out walking
  With a black thorn stick.

He was full of mischief,
  Full of glee.
He frightened all
  That he could see.

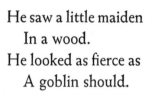

He saw a little maiden
  In a wood.
He looked as fierce as
  A goblin should.

He crept by the hedge row,
  He said, "Boo!"
"Boo!" laughed the little girl,
  "How are you?"

"What?" said the goblin,
  "Aren't you afraid?"
"I think you're funny,"
  Said the maid.

"Ha!" said the goblin,
  Sitting down flat.
"You think I'm funny?
  I don't like that.

"I'm very frightening.
  You should flee!"
"You're cunning," she said,
  "As you can be!"

Then she laughed again, and
  Went away.
But the goblin stood there
  All that day.

A beetle came by, and
  "Well?" it said.
But the goblin only
  Shook his head.

"For I am funny,"
  He said to it.
"I thought I was alarming,
  And I'm not a bit.

"If I'm amusing,"
  He said to himself,
"I won't be a goblin,
  I'll be an elf!

"For a goblin must be goblin
  All the day,
But an elf need only
  Dance and play."

So the little green goblin
  Became an elf.
And he dances all day and
  He likes himself.

WHAT THE WINDS BRING

EDMUND CLARENCE STEDMAN

Which is the Wind that brings the cold?
   The North Wind, Freddy, and all the snow
And the sheep will scamper into the fold
   When the North begins to blow.

Which is the Wind that brings the heat?
   The South Wind, Katy; and corn will grow
And peaches redden for you to eat,
   When the South begins to blow.

Which is the Wind that brings the rain?
   The East Wind, Arty; and farmers know
That cows come shivering up the lane
   When the East begins to blow.

Which is the Wind that brings the flowers?
   The West Wind, Bessy; and soft and low
The birdies sing in the summer hours
   When the West begins to blow.

TAXIS

RACHEL FIELD

Ho, for taxis green or blue,
  Hi, for taxis red,
They roll along the Avenue
  Like spools of colored thread!

  Jack-o'-lantern yellow,
  Orange as the moon,
  Greener than the greenest grass
  Ever grew in June.

  Gaily striped or checked in squares,
  Wheels that twinkle bright,
  Don't you think that taxis make
  A very pleasant sight?

  Taxis shiny in the rain,
  Scudding through the snow,
  Taxis flashing back the sun,
  Waiting in a row.

Ho, for taxis red and green,
  Hi, for taxis blue,
I wouldn't be a private car
  In sober black, would you?

THE COW

ROBERT LOUIS STEVENSON

The friendly cow all red and white,
  I love with all my heart:
She gives me cream with all her might,
  To eat with apple-tart.

She wanders lowing here and there,
  And yet she cannot stray,
All in the pleasant open air,
  The pleasant light of day.

And blown by all the winds that pass
  And wet with all the showers,
She walks among the meadow grass
  And eats the meadow flowers.

SERIOUS OMISSION

I know that there are dragons,
St. George's, Jason's, too,
And many modern dragons
With scales of green and blue;

But though I've been there many
    times
And carefully looked through,
I can't find a dragon
In the cages at the zoo!

               JOHN FARRAR

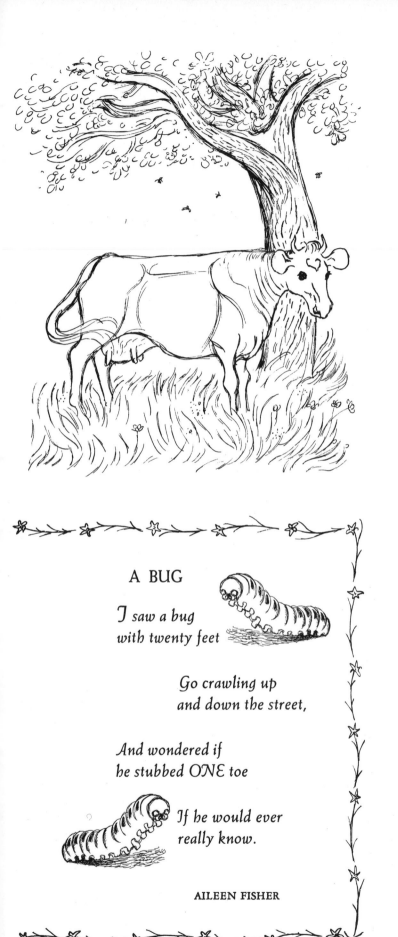

THE SWING

ROBERT LOUIS STEVENSON

How do you like to go up in a swing,
   Up in the air so blue?
Oh, I do think it the pleasantest thing
   Ever a child can do!

Up in the air and over the walls
   Till I can see so wide,
Rivers and trees and cattle and all
   Over the countryside—

Till I look down on the garden green,
   Down on the roof so brown—
Up in the air I go flying again,
   Up in the air and down!

A BUG

*I saw a bug
with twenty feet*

*Go crawling up
and down the street,*

*And wondered if
he stubbed ONE toe*

*If he would ever
really know.*

AILEEN FISHER

15

LITTLE ORPHANT ANNIE*

JAMES WHITCOMB RILEY

Inscribed with all faith and affection
*   To all the little children:—The happy ones,*
*   and sad ones;*
*   The sober and the silent ones; the boisterous*
*   and glad ones;*
*   The good ones—Yes, the good ones, too,*
*   and all the lovely bad ones.*

Little Orphant Annie's come to our house to stay,
An' wash the cups an' saucers up, an' brush the
  crumbs away,
An' shoo the chickens off the porch, an' dust the
  hearth, an' sweep,
An' make the fire, an' bake the bread, an' earn her
  board-an'-keep;
An' all us other childern, when the supper-things is
  done,
We set around the kitchen fire an' has the mostest
  fun
A-list'nin' to the witch-tales 'at Annie tells about,
An' the Gobble-uns 'at git you
            Ef you
                Don't
                    Watch
                        Out!

Onc't they wuz a little boy wouldn't say his
  prayers,—
An' when he went to bed at night, away upstairs,
His Mammy heerd him holler, an' his Daddy heerd
  him bawl,
An' when they turn't the kivvers down, he wuzn't
  there at all!
An' they seeked him in the rafter room, an' cubby-
  hole, an' press,
An' seeked him up the chimbly-flue, an' ever'-
  wheres, I guess;
But all they ever found wuz jist his pants an'
  roundabout:—

An' the Gobble-uns 'll git you
            Ef you
                Don't
                    Watch
                        Out!

An' one time a little girl 'us allus laugh an' grin,
An' make fun of ever'one, an' all her blood-an'-kin;
An' wunst, when they was "company," an' ole folks
  wuz there,
She mocked 'em an' shocked 'em, an' said she didn't
  care!
An' jist as she kicked her heels, an' turn't to run an'
  hide,
They wuz two great big Black Things a-standin' by
  her side,
An' they snatched her through the ceilin' 'fore she
  knowed what she's about!
An' the Gobble-uns 'll git you
            Ef you
                Don't
                    Watch
                        Out!

An' little Orphant Annie says, when the blaze is
  blue,
An' the lamp-wick sputters, an' the wind goes
  woo-oo!
An' you hear the crickets quit, an' the moon is gray,
An' the lightnin'-bugs in dew is all squenched
  away,—
You better mind yer parunts, an' yer teachurs fond
  an' dear,
An' churish them as loves you, an' dry the orphant's
  tear,
An' he'p the pore an' needy ones 'at clusters all
  about,
Er the Gobble-uns 'll git you
            Ef you
                Don't
                    Watch
                        Out!

THE OWL AND THE PUSSY-CAT

EDWARD LEAR

The Owl and the Pussy-Cat went to sea
   In a beautiful pea-green boat:
They took some honey, and plenty of money
   Wrapped up in a five-pound note.

The Owl looked up to the stars above,
   And sang to a small guitar,
"O lovely Pussy! O Pussy, my love,
   What a beautiful Pussy you are,
      You are, you are!
   What a beautiful Pussy you are!"

Pussy said to the Owl, "You elegant fowl!
   How charmingly sweet you sing!
O let us be married! too long we have tarried:
   But what shall we do for a ring?"

They sailed away for a year and a day,
   To the land where the Bong tree grows,
And there in a wood a Piggy-wig stood,
   With a ring at the end of his nose,
      His nose, his nose,
   With a ring at the end of his nose.

"Dear Pig, are you willing to sell for one shilling
   Your ring?" Said the Piggy, "I will."
So they took it away, and were married next day
   By the Turkey who lives on the hill.

They dined on mince, and slices of quince,
   Which they ate with a runcible spoon;
And hand in hand, on the edge of the sand,
   They danced by the light of the moon,
      The moon, the moon,
   They danced by the light of the moon.

THE LITTLE LAND

ROBERT LOUIS STEVENSON

When at home alone I sit
And am very tired of it,
   I have just to shut my eyes
   To go sailing through the skies—

To go sailing far away
To the pleasant Land of Play;
   To the fairy land afar
   Where the Little People are,
Where the clover tops are trees,
And the rain-pools are the seas.
   And the leaves like little ships
   Sail about on tiny trips;
And about the daisy tree
   Through the grasses
High o'erhead the bumblebee
   Hums and passes.

In that forest to and fro
I can wander, I can go;
   See the spider and the fly,
   And the ants go marching by,
Carrying parcels with their feet,
Down the green and grassy street.

   I can in the sorrel sit
   Where the ladybirds have lit;
I can climb the jointed grass,
   And on high
See the greater swallows pass
   In the sky!
And the round sun rolling by,
Heeding no such things as I.

Through the forest I can pass
Till, as in a looking-glass,
   Humming fly and daisy tree
   And my tiny self I see,
Painted very clear and neat
On the rain-pool at my feet.
   Should a leaflet come to land,
   Drifting near to where I stand,
Straight I'll board the tiny boat
Round the rain-pool sea to float.
   Little thoughtful creatures sit
   On the grassy coasts of it;

Little things with lovely eyes
See me sailing with surprise.
   Some are clad in armor green—
   These have sure to battle been!—

Some are pied with ev'ry hue,
Black and crimson, gold and blue;
   Some have wings and swift are gone;—
   But they all look kindly on.

When my eyes I once again
Open, and see all things plain;
   High bare walls, great bare floor;
Great big knobs on drawer and door;
Great big people perched on chairs,
Stitching tucks and mending tears,
   Each a hill that I could climb,
   And talking nonsense all the time—
     O dear me!
     That I could be
A sailor on the rain-pool sea,
A climber in the clover tree,
   And just come back, a sleepy head,
   Late at night to go to bed.

THE BABY GOES TO BOSTON

LAURA E. RICHARDS

What does the train say?
   Jiggle joggle, jiggle joggle!
What does the train say?
   Jiggle joggle jee!
Will the little baby go
Riding with the locomo?
Loky moky poky stoky
Smoky choky chee!

Ting! ting! the bells ring,
   Jiggle joggle, jiggle joggle!
Ting! ting! the bells ring,
   Jiggle joggle jee!
Ring for joy because we go
Riding with the locomo,
Loky moky poky stoky
   Smoky choky chee!

Look! how the trees run,
   Jiggle joggle, jiggle joggle!
Each chasing t'other one,
   Jiggle joggle jee!
Are they running for to go
Riding with the locomo?
Loky moky poky stoky
   Smoky choky chee!

Over the hills now,
   Jiggle joggle, jiggle joggle!
Down through the vale below,
   Jiggle joggle jee!

All the cows and horses run,
Crying, "Won't you take us on,
Loky moky poky stoky
   Smoky choky chee?"

So, so, the miles go,
   Jiggle joggle, jiggle joggle!
Now it's fast and now it's slow,
   Jiggle joggle jee!
When we're at our journey's end,
Say goodbye to snorting friend,
Loky moky poky stoky
   Smoky choky chee!

I'M GLAD

I'm glad the sky is painted blue,
And the earth is painted green,
With such a lot of nice fresh air
All sandwiched in between.
           ANONYMOUS

SALLY AND MANDA

Sally and Manda are two little lizards
Who gobble up flies in their two little
*   gizzards.*
They live by a toadstool near two
*   little hummocks*
And crawl all around on their two
*   little stomachs.*

ALICE B. CAMPBELL

THE WOODPECKER

ELIZABETH MADOX ROBERTS

The woodpecker pecked out a little round hole
And made him a house in the telephone pole.
One day when I watched he poked out his head,
And he had on a hood and a collar of red.
When the streams of rain pour out of the sky,
And the sparkles of lightning go flashing by,
And the big, big wheels of thunder roll,
He can snuggle back in the telephone pole.

WATER NOISES

ELIZABETH MADOX ROBERTS

When I am playing by myself,
And all the boys are lost around,
Then I can hear the water go;
It makes a little talking sound.

Along the rocks below the tree,
I see it ripple up and wink;
And I can hear it saying on,
"And do you think? And do you think?"

A bug shoots by that snaps and ticks,
And a bird flies up beside the tree
To go into the sky to sing.
I hear it say, "Killdee, killdee!"

Or else a yellow cow comes down
To splash a while and have a drink.
But when she goes I still can hear
The water say, "And do you think?"

MOON SONG

MILDRED PLEW MEIGS

Zoon, zoon, cuddle and croon—
　Over the crinkling sea,
The moon man flings him a silvered net
　Fashioned of moonbeams three.

And some folk say when the net lies long
　And the midnight hour is ripe;
The moon man fishes for some old song
　That fell from a sailor's pipe.

And some folk say that he fishes the bars
　Down where the dead ships lie,
Looking for lost little baby stars
　That slid from the slippery sky.

And the waves roll out and the waves roll in
　And the nodding night wind blows,
But why the moon man fishes the sea
　Only the moon man knows.

Zoon, zoon, net of the moon
　Rides on the wrinkling sea;
Bright is the fret and shining wet,
　Fashioned of moonbeams three.

And some folk say when the great net gleams
　And the waves are dusky blue,
The moon man fishes for two little dreams
　He lost when the world was new.

And some folk say in the late night hours,
　While the long fin-shadows slide,
The moon man fishes for cold sea flowers
　Under the tumbling tide.

And the waves roll out and the waves roll in
　And the gray gulls dip and doze,
But why the moon man fishes the sea
　Only the moon man knows.

Zoon, zoon, cuddle and croon—
　Over the crinkling sea,
The moon man flings him a silvered net
　Fashioned of moonbeams three.

And some folk say that he follows the flecks
　Down where the last light flows,
Fishing for two round gold-rimmed "specs"
　That blew from his button-like nose.

And some folk say while the salt sea foams
　And the silver net lines snare,
The moon man fishes for carven combs
　That float from the mermaids' hair.

And the waves roll out and the waves roll in
　And the nodding night wind blows,
But why the moon man fishes the sea
　Only the moon man knows.

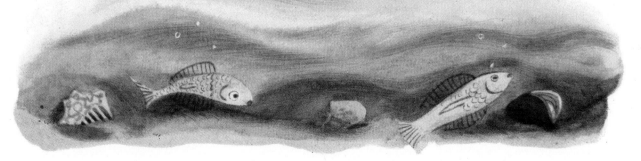

JONATHAN BING DANCES FOR SPRING

BEATRICE CURTIS BROWN

Who can ever stop him?
Who so fast as Bing?
When hop and prance, he does his dance
To celebrate the Spring.

Blow the fife and clarinet,
Let the band advance!
Mr. Bing will welcome Spring
With his festive dance!

Waking with the sunshine,
Starting out of sleep;
Flings away the blanket grey,
Makes a mighty leap—

Hop! He's on a tree top.
Bump! He's on the tiles.
Bounce and vault and somersault,
He goes for miles and miles.

The motor cars are hooting;
The whistles all a-blow,
They holler, "Hi!" as Bing goes by,
"Say, where d'you think you go?"

Leaps upon the mantelpiece,
Bounces up again,
Turns about and dashes out
Through the windowpane:

The Lord Mayors of the city
In velvet cloak and chain
Appear in state, expostulate
With Bing—but all in vain.

"Away, you foolish creatures!"
Cries happy Mr. Bing.
"With all this fun of flowers and sun
Who would not dance for spring?"

All the neighbors' children
Clap and shout, "Hooray!"
When Mr. B, in highest glee
Comes prancing down the way.

MR. NOBODY
ANONYMOUS

I know a funny little man,
     As quiet as a mouse,
Who does the mischief that is done
     In everybody's house!
There's no one ever sees his face,
     And yet we all agree
That every plate we break was cracked
     By Mr. Nobody.

 Tis he who always tears out books,
     Who leaves the door ajar,
He pulls the buttons from our shirts,
     And scatters pins afar;
That squeaking door will always squeak,
     For prithee, don't you see,
We leave the oiling to be done
     By Mr. Nobody.

The finger marks upon the door
     By none of us are made;
We never leave the blinds unclosed,
     To let the curtains fade.
The ink we never spill; the boots
     That lying round you see
Are not our boots;—they all belong
     To Mr. Nobody.

WHAT THE TOYS ARE THINKING
FFRIDA WOLFE

In the jolly, jolly Spring
When we long to leave the shop,
It's the most exciting thing
When any of you stop
And stare and ask the price
Of a Teddy or a top,
Or a baby-doll or Bunny,
Or a little speckled horse.
O, we think it's very nice
When you stand behind the nurses
Counting out what's in your purses;
We are watching you, of course,
Wond'ring what you mean to do,
Hoping, hoping you've the money
And can take us back with you.
But supposing you have not
Quite enough (we cost a lot),
Shake a paw then, stroke a head,
Pat a wistful nose instead,
Whisper in a furry ear,
Comfort us for what we're missing,—
Nursery tea and bedtime kissing—
All that never happens here.
You would find it slow yourselves
Sitting still all day on shelves.

Well, next time you're passing through
You'll remember what to do.

27

WYNKEN, BLYNKEN, AND NOD
EUGENE FIELD

Wynken, Blynken, and Nod one night
   Sailed off in a wooden shoe—
Sailed on a river of crystal light,
   Into a sea of dew.
"Where are you going, and what do you wish?"
   The old moon asked the three.
"We have come to fish for the herring fish
That live in this beautiful sea;
Nets of silver and gold have we!"
      Said Wynken,
      Blynken,
      And Nod.

The old moon laughed and sang a song,
   As they rocked in the wooden shoe,
And the wind that sped them all night long
   Ruffled the waves of dew.
The little stars were the herring fish
   That lived in that beautiful sea—
"Now cast your nets wherever you wish—
   Never afeard are we!"
   So cried the stars to the fishermen three:
      Wynken,
      Blynken,
      And Nod.

All night long their nets they threw
    To the stars in the twinkling foam—
Then down from the skies came the wooden shoe,
    Bringing the fishermen home;
'Twas all so pretty a sail it seemed
    As if it could not be,
And some folks thought 'twas a dream they'd
      dreamed
    Of sailing that beautiful sea—
But I shall name you the fishermen three:
        Wynken,
        Blynken,
        And Nod.

Wynken and Blynken are two little eyes,
    And Nod is a little head,
And the wooden shoe that sailed the skies
    Is a wee one's trundle-bed.
So shut your eyes while mother sings
    Of wonderful sights that be,
And you shall see the beautiful things
    As you rock in the misty sea,
    Where the old shoe rocked the fishermen
      three:
        Wynken,
        Blynken,
        And Nod.

BILLY GOATS CHEW
RICHARD W. EMERY

The billy goat would like to chew
Your picture book or shirt or shoe.
He eats the laundry off the line.
He likes the taste of sticks and twine.

His whiskers wiggle on his chin.
He doesn't REALLY swallow TIN.
The nanny goat is billy's bride.
They chew the laundry side by side.

THE NAUGHTY BOY
JOHN KEATS

There was a naughty boy,
And a naughty boy was he,
He ran away to Scotland
The people for to see—
Then he found
That the ground
Was as hard,
That a yard
Was as long,
That a song
Was as merry,

That a cherry
Was as red,
That lead
Was as weighty,
That fourscore
Was as eighty,
That a door
Was as wooden
As in England—
So he stood in his shoes
And he wonder'd,
He wonder'd,
He stood in his shoes
And he wonder'd.

DAISIES
FRANK DEMPSTER SHERMAN

At evening when I go to bed
I see the stars shine overhead;
They are the little daisies white
That dot the meadow of the Night.

And often while I'm dreaming so,
Across the sky the Moon will go;

It is a lady, sweet and fair,
Who comes to gather daisies there.

For, when at morning I arise,
There's not a star left in the skies;
She's picked them all and dropped them down
Into the meadows of the town.

FIREFLY

A little light is going by,
Is going up to see the sky,
A little light with wings.

I never could have thought of it,
To have a little bug all lit
And made to go on wings.

ELIZABETH MADOX ROBERTS

TEA PARTY
AILEEN FISHER

We had crackers
And cambric tea
And a roll divided
Between us three;

We had sugar
And milk for cream
(That tasted better
Than it would seem).

We poured the tea
From an elephant pot
And it burned our tongues
(Though it wasn't hot);

And we felt sorry
When Evelyn said,
"My favorite doll
Has a cold-in-the head."

RADIATOR LIONS
DOROTHY ALDIS

George lives in an apartment, and
His mother will not let
Him keep a dog or polliwog
Or rabbit for a pet.

So he has Radiator Lions.
(The parlor is the zoo.)
They love to fight, but will not bite
Unless he tells them to.

And days when it is very cold,
And he can't go outdoors,
They glower and they lower and they
Crouch upon all fours.

And roar most awful roarings and
Gurgle loud and mad.
Up their noses water goeses—
That's what makes them bad.

But he loves Radiator Lions!
He's glad, although they're wild,
He hasn't dogs or polliwogs
Like any other child!

THE FROG*

Be kind and tender to the Frog,
And do not call him names,
As "Slimy-skin," or "Polly-wog,"
Or likewise "Uncle James,"
Or "Gape-a-grin," or "Toad-gone-
wrong,"
Or "Billy Bandy-knees":
The frog is justly sensitive
To epithets like these.

No animal will more repay
A treatment kind and fair,
At least, so lonely people say
Who keep a frog (and by the way,
They are extremely rare).

HILAIRE BELLOC

*Reprinted from *The Bad Child's Book of Beasts* by Hilaire Belloc, by permission of and special arrangement with Alfred A. Knopf, Inc.

31

THE RAGGEDY MAN*

JAMES WHITCOMB RILEY

O The Raggedy Man! He works for Pa;
An' he's the goodest man ever you saw!
He comes to our house every day,
An' waters the horses, an' feeds 'em hay;
An' he opens the shed—an' we all ist laugh
When he drives out our little old wobbly calf;
An' nen—ef our hired girl says he can—
He milks the cow for 'Lizabuth Ann.—
    Ain't he a' awful good Raggedy Man?
      Raggedy! Raggedy! Raggedy Man!

W'y, The Raggedy Man—he's ist so good
He splits the kindlin' an' chops the wood;
An' nen he spades in our garden, too,
An' does most things 'at boys can't do!—
He clumbed clean up in our big tree
An' shooked a' apple down fer me—
An' nother'n, too, fer 'Lizabuth Ann—
An' nother'n, too, fer The Raggedy Man—
    Ain't he a' awful kind Raggedy Man?
      Raggedy! Raggedy! Raggedy Man!

An' The Raggedy Man, he knows most rhymes
An' tells 'em, ef I be good, sometimes:
Knows 'bout Giunts, an' Griffuns, an' Elves,
An' the Squidgicum-Squees 'at swallers therselves!
An', wite by the pump in our pasture-lot,
He showed me the hole 'at the Wunks is got,
'At lives 'way deep in the ground, an' can
Turn into me, er 'Lizabuth Ann!
    Ain't he a funny old Raggedy Man?
      Raggedy! Raggedy! Raggedy Man!

The Raggedy Man—one time when he
Wuz makin' a little bow-'n'-orry fer me,
Says, "When you're big like your Pa is,
Air you go' to keep a fine store like his—
An' be a rich merchunt—an' wear fine clothes?—
Er what air you go' to be, goodness knows!"
An' nen he laughed at 'Lizabuth Ann,
An' I says, " 'M go' to be a Raggedy Man!
    I'm ist go' to be a nice Raggedy Man!
      Raggedy! Raggedy! Raggedy Man!"

GRASSHOPPER GREEN

ANONYMOUS

Grasshopper green is a comical chap;
    He lives on the best of fare.
Bright little trousers, jacket, and cap,
    These are his summer wear.
Out in the meadow he loves to go,
    Playing away in the sun;
It's hopperty, skipperty, high and low,
    Summer's the time for fun.

Grasshopper green has a quaint little house;
    It's under the hedge so gay.
Grandmother Spider, as still as a mouse,
    Watches him over the way.
Gladly he's calling the children, I know,
    Out in the beautiful sun;
It's hopperty, skipperty, high and low,
    Summer's the time for fun.

MUD

Mud is very nice to feel

All squishing out between the toes.

I'd rather squish around in mud

Than smell a yellow rose.

Nobody else but the rosebush knows

How nice mud feels between the toes.
    POLLY CHASE BOYDEN

THE LITTLE BIRD

Once I saw a little bird
    Come hop, hop, hop;
So I cried, "Little bird,
    Will you stop, stop, stop?"

And was going to the window
    To say, "How do you do?"
But he shook his little tail,
    And far away he flew.
    OLD NURSERY RHYME

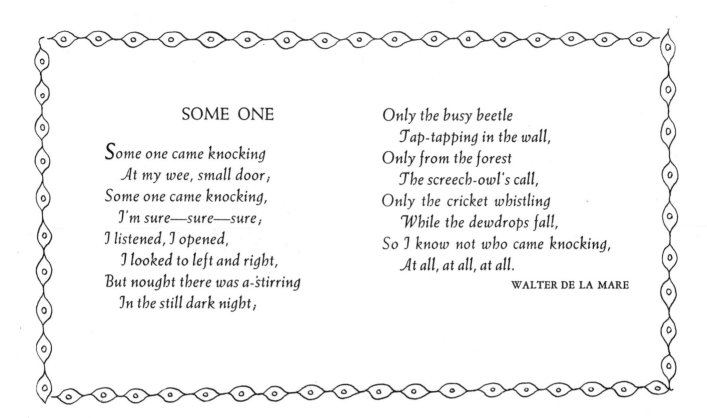

SOME ONE

Some one came knocking
  At my wee, small door;
Some one came knocking,
  I'm sure—sure—sure;
I listened, I opened,
  I looked to left and right,
But nought there was a-stirring
  In the still dark night;

Only the busy beetle
  Tap-tapping in the wall,
Only from the forest
  The screech-owl's call,
Only the cricket whistling
  While the dewdrops fall,
So I know not who came knocking,
  At all, at all, at all.

WALTER DE LA MARE

CHOOSING SHOES

FFRIDA WOLFE

New shoes, new shoes,
Red and pink and blue shoes,
Tell me, what would *you* choose
If they'd let us buy?

Buckle shoes, bow shoes,
Pretty pointy-toe shoes,
Strappy, cappy low shoes;
Let's have some to try.

Bright shoes, white shoes,
Dandy dance-by-night shoes,
Perhaps-a-little-tight shoes;
Like some? So would I.

BUT

Flat shoes, fat shoes,
Stump-along-like-that shoes,
Wipe-them-on-the-mat shoes,
O that's the sort they'll buy.

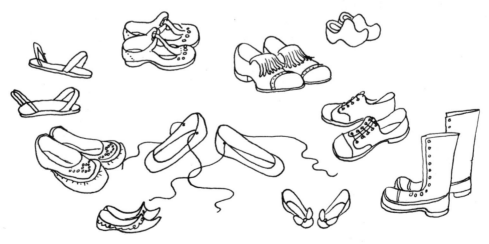

35

OVER THE HILLS AND FAR AWAY

OLD NURSERY RHYME

As Dolly was milking her cow one day,
Tom took out his pipe and began to play;
So Doll and the cow danced "the Cheshire round,"
Till the pail was broke and the milk ran on the ground.

Tom, Tom, the piper's son,
He learned to play when he was young;
But the only tune that he could play
Was "Over the hills and far away."

He met old Dame Trot with a basket of eggs,
He used his pipe and she used her legs;
She danced about till the eggs were all broke,
She began to fret, but he laughed at the joke.

Now Tom with his pipe made such a noise
That he pleased both the girls and boys,
And they all stopped to hear him play
"Over the hills and far away."

He saw a cross fellow was beating an ass,
Heavy laden with pots, pans, dishes, and glass;
He took out his pipe and played them a tune,
And the jackass's load was lightened soon.

Tom with his pipe did play with such skill
That those who heard him could never keep still;
Whenever they heard they began to dance,
Even pigs on their hind legs would after him prance.

36

THE LITTLE SHEPHERDESS
TO HER LAMBS

ROSE FYLEMAN

Dance, my dearies, dance, my pretties,
In a snowy ring;
I will pipe the merry ditties
That the fairies sing.
Blackbirds, thrushes, linnets, starlings—
They will pipe them, too,
And the little winds, my darlings,
All shall dance with you.

Dance, my dearies, dance, my pretties,
On the daisied floors;
Only in the smoky cities
Folk are still indoors.
All along the meadow highways
Leap and skip and prance;
All among the elfin byways
Dance, my dearies, dance.

THE WALRUS AND THE CARPENTER

LEWIS CARROLL

The sun was shining on the sea,
   Shining with all his might:
He did his very best to make
   The billows smooth and bright—
And this was odd, because it was
   The middle of the night.

The moon was shining sulkily,
   Because she thought the sun
Had got no business to be there
   After the day was done—
"It's very rude of him," she said,
   "To come and spoil the fun!"

The sea was wet as wet could be,
   The sands were dry as dry.
You could not see a cloud, because
   No cloud was in the sky:
No birds were flying overhead—
   There were no birds to fly.

The Walrus and the Carpenter
   Were walking close at hand:
They wept like anything to see
   Such quantities of sand:
"If this were only cleared away,"
   They said, "it would be grand!"

"If seven maids with seven mops
   Swept it for half a year,
Do you suppose," the Walrus said,
   "That they could get it clear?"
"I doubt it," said the Carpenter,
   And shed a bitter tear.

"O Oysters, come and walk with us!"
   The Walrus did beseech.
"A pleasant walk, a pleasant talk,
   Along the briny beach:
We cannot do with more than four,
   To give a hand to each."

The eldest Oyster looked at him,
   But never a word he said:
The eldest Oyster winked his eye,
   And shook his heavy head—
Meaning to say he did not choose
   To leave the oyster-bed.

But four young Oysters hurried up,
   All eager for the treat:
Their coats were brushed, their faces washed,
   Their shoes were clean and neat—
And this was odd, because, you know,
   They hadn't any feet.

Four other Oysters followed them,
    And yet another four;
And thick and fast they came at last,
    And more, and more, and more—
All hopping through the frothy waves,
    And scrambling to the shore.

The Walrus and the Carpenter
    Walked on a mile or so,
And then they rested on a rock
    Conveniently low:
And all the little Oysters stood
    And waited in a row.

"The time has come," the Walrus said,
    "To talk of many things:
Of shoes—and ships—and sealing wax—
    Of cabbages—and kings—
And why the sea is boiling hot—
    And whether pigs have wings."

"But wait a bit," the Oysters cried,
    "Before we have our chat;
For some of us are out of breath,
    And all of us are fat!"
"No hurry!" said the Carpenter.
    They thanked him much for that.

"A loaf of bread," the Walrus said,
    "Is what we chiefly need:
Pepper and vinegar besides
    Are very good indeed—
Now, if you're ready, Oysters dear,
    We can begin to feed."

"But not on us!" the Oysters cried,
    Turning a little blue.
"After such kindness, that would be
    A dismal thing to do!"
"The night is fine," the Walrus said.
    "Do you admire the view?

"It was so kind of you to come!
    And you are very nice!"
The Carpenter said nothing but
    "Cut us another slice.
I wish you were not quite so deaf—
    I've had to ask you twice!"

"It seems a shame," the Walrus said,
    "To play them such a trick.
After we've brought them out so far,
    And made them trot so quick."
The Carpenter said nothing but
    "The butter's spread too thick!"

"I weep for you," the Walrus said:
    "I deeply sympathize."
With sobs and tears he sorted out
    Those of the largest size,
Holding his pocket-handkerchief
    Before his streaming eyes.

"O Oysters," said the Carpenter,
    "You've had a pleasant run!
Shall we be trotting home again?"
    But answer came there none—
And this was scarcely odd, because
    They'd eaten every one.

GENERAL STORE
RACHEL FIELD

Some day I'm going to have a store
With a tinkly bell hung over the door,
With real glass cases and counters wide
And drawers all spilly with things inside.
There'll be a little of everything:
Bolts of calico; balls of string;
Jars of peppermint; tins of tea;
Pots and kettles and crockery;

Seeds in packets; scissors bright;
Kegs of sugar, brown and white;
Sarsaparilla for picnic lunches,
Bananas and rubber boots in bunches.
I'll fix the window and dust each shelf,
And take the money in all myself.
It will be my store, and I will say:
"What can I do for you today?"

40

THE ANIMAL STORE

RACHEL FIELD

If I had a hundred dollars to spend,
  Or maybe a little more,
I'd hurry as fast as my legs would go
  Straight to the animal store.

I wouldn't say, "How much for this or that?"
  "What kind of a dog is he?"
I'd buy as many as rolled an eye,
  Or wagged a tail at me!

I'd take the hound with the drooping ears
  That sits by himself alone;
Cockers and Cairns and wobbly pups
  For to be my very own.

I might buy a parrot all red and green,
  And the monkey I saw before,
If I had a hundred dollars to spend,
  Or maybe a little more.

41

FOR CHRISTMAS
DOROTHY ALDIS

I want a Puppy Dog

Not made of wool.

I want a Nanny Goat

I don't have to pull;

I want a Kitty Cat

I don't have to wind.

And I want an Elephant

Can sit DOWN behind.

THE PEOPLE

The ants are walking under the
  ground,
And the pigeons are flying on
  the steeple,
And in between are the people.
ELIZABETH MADOX ROBERTS

THE SEA SHELL

Sea Shell, Sea Shell,
  Sing me a song, O please!
A song of ships, and sailor men,
  Of parrots and tropical trees;
Of islands lost in the Spanish
  Main
Which no man ever may find
  again,
Of fishes and corals under the
  waves,
And sea-horses stabled in great
  green caves—
Sea Shell, Sea Shell,
Sing of the things you know
  so well.
AMY LOWELL

FROM A RAILWAY CARRIAGE
ROBERT LOUIS STEVENSON

Faster than fairies, faster than witches,
Bridges and houses, hedges and ditches;

And charging along like troops in a battle
All through the meadows the horses and cattle;

All of the sights of the hill and the plain
Fly as thick as driving rain;

And ever again, in the wink of an eye,
Painted stations whistle by.

Here is a child who clambers and scrambles,
All by himself and gathering brambles;

Here is a tramp who stands and gazes;
And there is the green for stringing the daisies!

Here is a cart run away in the road,
Lumping along with man and load;

And here is a mill, and there is a river:
Each a glimpse and gone for ever!

DIFFERENCES
ROSE FYLEMAN

Daddy goes a-riding in a motor painted grey,
He makes a lot of snorty noise before he gets away;
The fairies go a-riding when they wish to take their
    ease,
The fairies go a-riding on the backs of bumblebees.

Daddy goes a-sailing in a jolly wooden boat,
He takes a lot of tackle and his very oldest coat;

The fairies go a-sailing, and I wonder they get home,
The fairies go a-sailing on a little scrap of foam.

Daddy goes a-climbing with a knapsack and a stick,
The rocks are very hard and steep, his boots are
    very thick;
But the fairies go a-climbing (I've seen them there in
    crowds),
The fairies go a-climbing on the mountains in the
    clouds.

OTHERWISE

There must be magic,
Otherwise,
How could day turn to night?
And how could sailboats,
Otherwise,
Go sailing out of sight?
And how could peanuts,
Otherwise,
Be covered up so tight?
    AILEEN FISHER

LITTLE WIND

Little wind, blow on the hilltop,
Little wind, blow on the plain;
Little wind, blow up the sunshine,
Little wind, blow off the rain.
    KATE GREENAWAY

GROWING UP
MARCHETTE GAYLORD CHUTE

When I grow up I'll carry a stick
    And be very dignified,
I'll have a watch that will really tick,
My house will be tall and built of brick,
And no one will guess that it's just a trick,
    And I'm really myself inside.

THE SUGAR-PLUM TREE

EUGENE FIELD

Have you ever heard of the Sugar-Plum Tree?
 'Tis a marvel of great renown!
It blooms on the shore of the Lollipop Sea
 In the garden of Shut-Eye Town;
The fruit that it bears is so wondrously sweet
 (As those who have tasted it say)
That good little children have only to eat
 Of that fruit to be happy next day.

When you've got to the tree, you would have a
 hard time
 To capture the fruit which I sing;
The tree is so tall that no person could climb
 To the boughs where the sugar-plums swing!
But up in that tree sits a chocolate cat,
 And a gingerbread dog prowls below—
And this is the way you contrive to get at
 Those sugar-plums tempting you so:

You say but the word to that gingerbread dog
 And he barks with such terrible zest
That the chocolate cat is at once all agog,
 As her swelling proportions attest.
And the chocolate cat goes cavorting around
 From this leafy limb unto that,
And the sugar-plums tumble, of course, to the
 ground—
 Hurrah for that chocolate cat!

There are marshmallows, gumdrops, and pepper-
 mint canes,
 With stripings of scarlet or gold,
And you carry away of the treasure that rains
 As much as your apron can hold!
So come, little child, cuddle closer to me
 In your dainty white nightcap and gown,
And I'll rock you away to that Sugar-Plum Tree
 In the garden of Shut-Eye Town.

COLOR

What is pink? a rose is pink
By a fountain's brink.
What is red? a poppy's red
In its barley bed.
What is blue? the sky is blue
Where the clouds float thro'.
What is white? a swan is white
Sailing in the light.
What is yellow? pears are yellow,
Rich and ripe and mellow.
What is green? the grass is green,
With small flowers between.
What is violet? clouds are violet
In the summer twilight.
What is orange? Why, an orange,
Just an orange!

CHRISTINA G. ROSSETTI

VERY NEARLY
QUEENIE SCOTT-HOPPER

I never quite saw fairy-folk
　　A-dancing in the glade,
Where, just beyond the hollow oak,
　　Their broad green rings are laid;
But, while behind that oak I hid,
One day I very nearly did!

I never quite saw mermaids rise
　　Above the twilight sea,
When sands, left wet, 'neath sunset skies,
　　Are blushing rosily:
But—all alone, those rocks amid—
One day I very nearly did!

I never quite saw Goblin Grim,
　　Who haunts our lumber room
And pops his head above the rim
　　Of that oak chest's deep gloom:
But once—when Mother raised the lid—
　　I very, very nearly did!

WHO

HAS

SEEN

THE

WIND?

Who has seen the wind?
　　Neither I nor you:
But when the leaves hang trembling,
　　The wind is passing through.

Who has seen the wind?
　　Neither you nor I:
But when the trees bow down their
　　heads,
　　The wind is passing by.

CHRISTINA G. ROSSETTI

MOUSE*

Little Mouse in gray velvet,
Have you had a cheese-breakfast?
There are no crumbs on your coat,
Did you use a napkin?
I wonder what you had to eat,
And who dresses you in gray
　　velvet?

HILDA CONKLING

*Reprinted with permission from *Poems by a Little Girl* by Hilda Conkling. Copyright, 1920, by J. B. Lippincott Company.

SPRING SIGNS
MILDRED BOWERS ARMSTRONG

Everywhere the wind blows
There goes spring—
Red kites and green kites
Are tugging at the string.

Walks have hardly dried
Until marbles roll about
Long before the colored flowers
In the fields are out.

Maybe there is frost yet
And a touch of snow,
But there are little spring signs
Where the children go.

THE ELF AND THE DORMOUSE

OLIVER HERFORD

Under a toadstool crept a wee Elf,
Out of the rain, to shelter himself.

Under the toadstool, sound asleep,
Sat a big Dormouse all in a heap.

Trembled the wee Elf, frightened, and yet
Fearing to fly away lest he get wet.

To the next shelter—maybe a mile!
Sudden the wee Elf smiled a wee smile,

Tugged till the toadstool toppled in two,
Holding it over him, gayly he flew.

Soon he was safe home, dry as could be,
Soon woke the Dormouse—"Good gracious me!

Where is my toadstool?" loud he lamented.
And that's how umbrellas first were invented.

WHERE GO THE BOATS

ROBERT LOUIS STEVENSON

Dark brown is the river.
    Golden is the sand.
It flows along forever,
    With trees on either hand.

Green leaves a-floating,
    Castles of the foam,
Boats of mine a-boating—
    Where will all come home?

On goes the river
    And out past the mill,
Away down the valley,
    Away down the hill.

Away down the river,
    A hundred miles or more,
Other little children
    Shall bring my boats ashore.

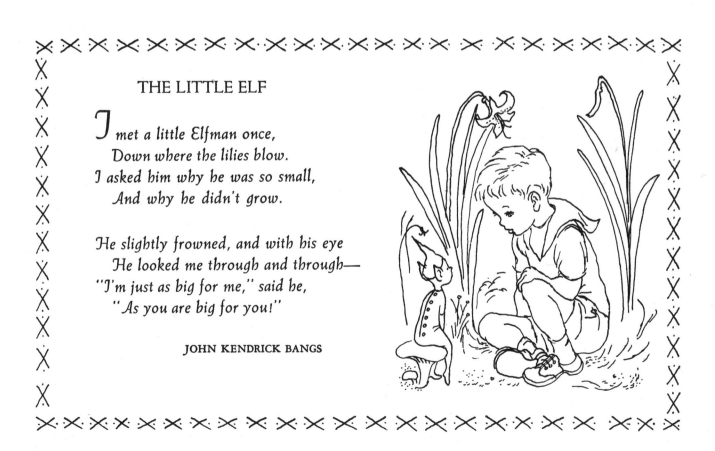

THE LITTLE ELF

I met a little Elfman once,
    Down where the lilies blow.
I asked him why he was so small,
    And why he didn't grow.

He slightly frowned, and with his eye
    He looked me through and through—
"I'm just as big for me," said he,
    "As you are big for you!"

JOHN KENDRICK BANGS

THE THREE JOVIAL HUNTSMEN

OLD BALLAD

There were three jovial huntsmen, and a-hunting
they did go;
And they hunted, and they holloed, and they blew
their horns also.
> Look ye there!

And one said, "Mind your eyes and keep your
noses right in the wind.
And then by scent or sight we'll light on something
to our mind."
> Look ye there!

They hunted and they holloed, and the first thing
they did find
Was a tattered scarecrow in a field, and that they
left behind.
> Look ye there!

One said it was a scarecrow, and another he said,
"Nay,
It's just a gentleman farmer that has gone and lost
his way."
> Look ye there!

They hunted and they holloed, and the next thing
they did find
Was a grunting, grinding grindstone, and that they
left behind.
> Look ye there!

One said it was a grindstone, another he said, "Nay,
It's nothing but an old spoiled cheese, that some-
body's rolled away."
> Look ye there!

They hunted and they holloed, and the next thing
they did find
Was a bull-calf in a barnyard, and that, too, they
left behind.
> Look ye there!

One said it was a bull-calf, and another he said,
"Nay,
It's just a painted jackass, that has never learned to
bray."
> Look ye there!

They hunted and they holloed, and the next thing
    they did find
Was two-three children leaving school, and these
    they left behind.
        Look ye there!

One said that they were children, but another he
    said, "Nay,
They're naught but little angels, so we'll leave 'em
    to their play."
        Look ye there!

They hunted, and they holloed, and the next thing
    they did find
Was a fat pig smiling in a ditch, and that, too, they
    left behind.
        Look ye there!

One said it was a fat pig, but another he said, "Nay,
It's just a Lunnon Alderman, whose clothes are
    stolen away."
        Look ye there!

They hunted, and they holloed, and the next thing
    they did find
Was two young lovers in a lane, and these they left
    behind.
        Look ye there!

One said that they were lovers, but another he said,
    "Nay,
They're two poor wandering lunatics—come, let us
    go away."
        Look ye there!

So they hunted and they holloed, till the setting of
    the sun,
And they'd nothing to bring home at last, when the
    hunting day was done.
        Look ye there!

Then one unto the other said, "This hunting doesn't
    pay,
But we've cantered up and down a bit, and had a
    rattling day!"
        Look ye there!

MY SHADOW
ROBERT LOUIS STEVENSON

I have a little shadow that goes in and out with me,
And what can be the use of him is more than I can see.
He is very, very like me from the heels up to the head;
And I see him jump before me, when I jump into my bed.

The funniest thing about him is the way he likes to grow—
Not at all like proper children, which is always very slow;
For he sometimes shoots up taller like an india-rubber ball,
And he sometimes gets so little that there's none of him at all.

He hasn't got a notion of how children ought to play,
And can only make a fool of me in every sort of way.
He stays so close beside me, he's a coward you can see;
I'd think shame to stick to nursie as that shadow sticks to me!

One morning, very early, before the sun was up,
I rose and found the shining dew on every buttercup;
But my lazy little shadow, like an errant sleepy-head,
Had stayed at home behind me and was fast asleep in bed.

MICE
ROSE FYLEMAN

I think mice
Are rather nice.

    Their tails are long,
    Their faces small,
    They haven't any
    Chins at all.
    Their ears are pink,
    Their teeth are white,
    They run about
    The house at night.
    They nibble things
    They shouldn't touch
    And no one seems
    To like them much.

But I think mice
Are nice.

EXTREMES*

*A little boy once played so loud
That the thunder up in a thundercloud,
Said, "Since I can't be heard, why, then
I'll never, never, thunder again!"*

*And a little girl once kept so still
That she heard a fly on the window sill
Whisper and say to a ladybird,—
"She's the stillest child I ever heard!"*

          JAMES WHITCOMB RILEY

*From *The Book of Joyous Children* by James Whitcomb Riley, copyright 1902, used by special permission of the publishers, The Bobbs-Merrill Company.

THE SECRET
MARCHETTE GAYLORD CHUTE

    I know where there's a treasure
        Down behind the shed.
    I think about it often
        After I go to bed.

    Three steps north of the corn crib,
        Down in the roots of a tree,
    That's where the pirates hid it,
        All most secretly.

Tomorrow I'll get a shovel
    And go and dig it up;
And then I'll keep it always,
    Safe in a kitchen cup.

THE PICNIC

They had a picnic in the woods,
And Mother couldn't go that day,
But the twins and Brother and I could
    go,
We rode on the wagon full of hay.

There were more little girls than ten,
    I guess.
And the boy that is Joe B. Kirk
    was there.
He found a toad and a katydid,
And a little girl came whose name
    was Clare.

Miss Kate-Marie made us play a
    song
Called "Fare-you-well, says
    Johnny O'Brown."
You dance in a ring and sing it
    through,
And then someone kneels down.

She kissed us all and
    Joe B. Kirk;
But Joe B. didn't mind a bit.
He walked around and swung his
    arms
And seemed to be very glad of it.

Then Mr. Jim said he would play,
But Miss Marie, she told him then,
It's a game for her and the little folks,
And he could go and fish with the
    men.

            ELIZABETH MADOX ROBERTS

THE CAMEL'S COMPLAINT
CHARLES E. CARRYL

"Canary-birds feed on sugar and seed,
   Parrots have crackers to crunch;
And, as for the poodles, they tell me the noodles
   Have chickens and cream for their lunch.
     But there's never a question
     About MY digestion—
       ANYTHING does for me!

"Cats, you're aware, can repose in a chair,
   Chickens can roost upon rails;
Puppies are able to sleep in a stable,
   And oysters can slumber in pails.
     But no one supposes
     A poor Camel dozes—
       ANY PLACE does for me!

"Lambs are inclosed where it's never exposed,
   Coops are constructed for hens;
Kittens are treated to houses well heated,
   And pigs are protected by pens.
     But a Camel comes handy
     Wherever it's sandy—
       ANYWHERE does for me!

"People would laugh if you rode a giraffe,
   Or mounted the back of an ox;
It's nobody's habit to ride on a rabbit,
   Or try to bestraddle a fox.
     But as for a Camel, he's
     Ridden by families—
       ANY LOAD does for me!

"A snake is as round as a hole in the ground,
   And weasels are wavy and sleek;
And no alligator could ever be straighter
   Than lizards that live in a creek.
     But a Camel's all lumpy
     And bumpy and humpy—
       ANY SHAPE does for me!"

THE LITTLE TURTLE*
VACHEL LINDSAY

There was a little turtle.
He lived in a box.
He swam in a puddle.
He climbed on the rocks.

He snapped at a mosquito.
He snapped at a flea.
He snapped at a minnow.
And he snapped at me.

He caught the mosquito.
He caught the flea.
He caught the minnow.
But he didn't catch me.

WHO LIKES THE RAIN?
CLARA DOTY BATES

"I," said the duck, "I call it fun,
For I have my little red rubbers on.
They make a cunning three-toed track
In the soft cool mud. Quack! Quack!"

"I," cried the dandelion, "I.
My roots are thirsty, my buds are dry."
And she lifted her little yellow head
Out of her green and grassy bed.

"I hope 'twill pour! I hope 'twill pour!"
Croaked the tree toad at his gray bark door.
"For with a broad leaf for a roof
I am perfectly weather-proof."

Sang the brook, "I welcome every drop;
Come, come, dear rain drops, never stop
Till a great river you make of me,
Then I will carry you to the sea."

*From *Collected Poems* by Vachel Lindsay, by permission of The Macmillan Company, publishers.

THE FIRST DAY OF CHRISTMAS

OLD ENGLISH CAROL

THE FIRST DAY of Christmas,
My true love sent to me
A partridge in a pear tree.

The second day of Christmas,
My true love sent to me
Two turtle doves, and
A partridge in a pear tree.

The third day of Christmas,
My true love sent to me
Three French hens,
Two turtle doves, and
A partridge in a pear tree.

The fourth day of Christmas,
My true love sent to me
Four colly birds,
Three French hens,
Two turtle doves, and
A partridge in a pear tree.

The fifth day of Christmas,
My true love sent to me
Five gold rings,
Four colly birds,
Three French hens,
Two turtle doves, and
A partridge in a pear tree.

The sixth day of Christmas,
My true love sent to me
Six geese a-laying,
Five gold rings,
Four colly birds,
Three French hens,
Two turtle doves, and
A partridge in a pear tree.

The seventh day of Christmas,
My true love sent to me
Seven swans a-swimming,
Six geese a-laying,
Five gold rings,
Four colly birds,
Three French hens,
Two turtle doves, and
A partridge in a pear tree.

The eighth day of Christmas,
My true love sent to me
Eight maids a-milking,
Seven swans a-swimming,
Six geese a-laying,
Five gold rings,
Four colly birds,
Three French hens,
Two turtle doves, and
A partridge in a pear tree.

The ninth day of Christmas,
My true love sent to me
Nine drummers drumming,
Eight maids a-milking,
Seven swans a-swimming,
Six geese a-laying,
Five gold rings,
Four colly birds,
Three French hens,
Two turtle doves, and
A partridge in a pear tree.

The tenth day of Christmas,
My true love sent to me
Ten pipers piping,
Nine drummers drumming,
Eight maids a-milking,
Seven swans a-swimming,
Six geese a-laying,
Five gold rings,
Four colly birds,
Three French hens,
Two turtle doves, and
A partridge in a pear tree.

The eleventh day of Christmas,
My true love sent to me
Eleven ladies dancing,
Ten pipers piping,
Nine drummers drumming,
Eight maids a-milking,
Seven swans a-swimming,
Six geese a-laying,
Five gold rings,
Four colly birds,
Three French hens,
Two turtle doves, and
A partridge in a pear tree.

The twelfth day of Christmas,
My true love sent to me
Twelve fiddlers fiddling,
Eleven ladies dancing,
Ten pipers piping,
Nine drummers drumming,
Eight maids a-milking,
Seven swans a-swimming,
Six geese a-laying,
Five gold rings,
Four colly birds,
Three French hens,
Two turtle doves, and
A partridge in a pear tree.

THE TALE OF CUSTARD, THE DRAGON

OGDEN NASH

Belinda lived in a little white house,
With a little black kitten and a little gray mouse,
And a little yellow dog and a little red wagon,
And a realio, trulio, little pet dragon.

Now the name of the little black kitten was Ink,
And the little gray mouse, she called her Blink,
And the little yellow dog was sharp as Mustard,
But the dragon was a coward, and she called him
    Custard.

Custard the dragon had big sharp teeth,
And spikes on top of him and scales underneath,
Mouth like a fireplace, chimney for a nose,
And realio, trulio, daggers on his toes.

Belinda was as brave as a barrel full of bears,
And Ink and Blink chased lions down the stairs,
Mustard was as brave as a tiger in a rage,
But Custard cried for a nice safe cage.

Belinda tickled him, she tickled him unmerciful,
Ink, Blink and Mustard, they rudely called him
    Percival,
They all sat laughing in the little red wagon
At the realio, trulio, cowardly dragon.

Belinda giggled till she shook the house,
And Blink said, "Weeek!" (which is giggling for a
    mouse),
Ink and Mustard rudely asked his age
When Custard cried for a nice safe cage.

Suddenly, suddenly they heard a nasty sound,
And Mustard growled, and they all looked around.
"Meowch!" cried Ink, and "Ooh!" cried Belinda,
For there was a pirate, climbing in the winda.

Pistol in his left hand, pistol in his right,
And he held in his teeth a cutlass bright,
His beard was black, one leg was wood;
It was clear that the pirate meant no good.

Belinda paled, and she cried, "Help! Help!"
But Mustard fled with a terrified yelp,
Ink trickled down to the bottom of the household
And little mouse Blink strategically mouseholed.

But up jumped Custard, snorting like an engine,
Clashed his tail like irons in a dungeon.
With a clatter and a clank and a jangling squirm
He went at the pirate like a robin at a worm.

The pirate gaped at Belinda's dragon,
And gulped some grog from his pocket flagon.
He fired two bullets, but they didn't hit,
And Custard gobbled him, every bit.

Belinda embraced him, Mustard licked him,
No one mourned for his pirate victim.
Ink and Blink in glee did gyrate
Around the dragon that ate the pirate.

Belinda still lives in her little white house,
With her little black kitten and her little gray
    mouse,
And her little yellow dog and her little red wagon,
And her realio, trulio, little pet dragon.

Belinda is as brave as a barrel full of bears,
And Ink and Blink chase lions down the stairs.
Mustard is as brave as a tiger in a rage,
But Custard keeps crying for a nice safe cage.

GYPSIES*

RACHEL FIELD

Last night the gypsies came—
Nobody knows from where.
Where they've gone to nobody knows,
And nobody seems to care!

Between the trees on the old swamp road
I saw them round their fire:
Tattered children and dogs that barked
As the flames leaped high and higher;
There were black-eyed girls in scarlet shawls,
Old folk wrinkled with years,
Men with handkerchiefs round their throats
And silver loops in their ears.
Ragged and red like maple leaves
When frost comes in the fall,
The gypsies stayed but a single night;
In the morning gone were all—
Never a shaggy gypsy dog.
Never a gypsy child;
Only a burnt-out gypsy fire
Where danced that band so wild.

All gone and away,
Who knows where?
Only the wind that sweeps
Maple branches bare.

*From *The Pointed People* by Rachel Field, by permission of The Macmillan Company, publishers.

MISS T.

WALTER DE LA MARE

It's a very odd thing—
    As odd as can be—
That whatever Miss T. eats
    Turns into Miss T.;
Porridge and apples,
    Mince, muffins and mutton,
Jam, junket, jumbles—
    Not a rap, not a button
It matters; the moment
    They're out of her plate,
Though shared by Miss Butcher
    And sour Mr. Bate;
Tiny and cheerful
    And as neat as can be,
Whatever Miss T. eats
    Turns into Miss T.

THE ICE MAN
DOROTHY ALDIS

I licked it and it felt so nice
And it dribbled down my dress
And "ARE YOU EATING UP MY ICE?"
The ice man said, and I said, "Yes."

"It's cold," I told him. "No!" he said,
And then he asked if I was four,
And what time must I go to bed
And did I take naps any more.

And I told him everything—
All the games I liked to play,
And the highest I could swing,
And the pieces I could say.

And he listened, looking so
Red and smiley in the face,
But then he said he had to go
And leave some ice another place.

THE LAND OF COUNTERPANE
ROBERT LOUIS STEVENSON

When I was sick and lay a-bed,
I had two pillows at my head,
And all my toys beside me lay
To keep me happy all the day.

And sometimes for an hour or so
I watched my leaden soldiers go,
With different uniforms and drills,
Among the bed-clothes, through the hills;

And sometimes sent my ships in fleets
All up and down among the sheets;
Or brought my trees and houses out,
And planted cities all about.

I was the giant great and still
That sits upon the pillow-hill
And sees before him, dale and plain,
The pleasant land of counterpane.

THE DUEL

EUGENE FIELD

1.

The gingham dog and the calico cat
   Side by side on the table sat;
   'Twas half-past twelve, and (what do you think!)
Nor one nor t'other had slept a wink!
   The old Dutch clock and the Chinese plate
   Appeared to know as sure as fate
There was going to be a terrible spat.
   (I wasn't there; I simply state
   What was told to me by the Chinese plate!)

2.

The gingham dog went, "Bow-wow-wow!"
And the calico cat replied, "Mee-ow!"
The air was littered, an hour or so,
With bits of gingham and calico,
   While the old Dutch clock in the chimney-place
   Up with its hands before its face,
For it always dreaded a family row!
   (Now mind: I'm only telling you
   What the old Dutch clock declares is true!)

3.

The Chinese plate looked very blue,
And wailed, "Oh, dear! what shall we do!"
But the gingham dog and the calico cat
Wallowed this way and tumbled that,
    Employing every tooth and claw
    In the awfullest way you ever saw—
And, oh! how the gingham and calico flew!
    (Don't fancy I exaggerate—
    I got my news from the Chinese plate!)

4.

Next morning, where the two had sat
They found no trace of dog or cat;
And some folks think unto this day
That burglars stole that pair away!
    But the truth about the cat and pup
    Is this: they ate each other up!
Now what do you really think of that?
    (The old Dutch clock, it told me so,
    And that is how I came to know.)

THE CUPBOARD
WALTER DE LA MARE

I know a little cupboard,
With a teeny tiny key,
And there's a jar of Lollypops
    For me, me, me.

It has a little shelf, my dear,
As dark as dark can be,
And there's a dish of Banbury Cakes
    For me, me, me.

I have a small fat grandmamma,
With a very slippery knee,
And she's Keeper of the Cupboard,
    With the key, key, key.

And when I'm very good, my dear,
As good as good can be,
There's Banbury Cakes, and Lollypops
    For me, me, me.

THE BEST GAME
THE
FAIRIES PLAY

The best game the fairies play,
    The best game of all,
Is sliding down steeples—
    (You know they're very tall)
You fly to the weathercock,
    And when you hear it crow,
You fold your wings and clutch your
        things
    And then let go!
They have a million other games—
    Cloud-catching's one,
And mud-mixing after rain
    Is heaps and heaps of fun;
But when you go and stay with them
    Never mind the rest,
Take my advice—they're very nice,
    But steeple-sliding's best!
                        ROSE FYLEMAN

Where in jungles, near and far,
Man-devouring tigers are,
Lying close and giving ear
Lest the hunt be drawing near,
Or a comer-by be seen
Swinging in a palanquin;—
Where among the desert sands
Some deserted city stands,
All its children, sweep and prince,
Grown to manhood ages since,
Not a foot in street or house
Not a stir of child or mouse,
And when kindly falls the night,
In all the town no spark of light.

TRAVEL

ROBERT LOUIS STEVENSON

I should like to rise and go
Where the golden apples grow;—
Where below another sky
Parrot islands anchored lie,
And, watched by cockatoos and goats,
Lonely Crusoes building boats;—
Where in sunshine reaching out
Eastern cities, miles about,
Are with mosque and minaret
Among sandy gardens set,
And the rich goods from near and far
Hang for sale in the bazaar;—
Where the Great Wall round China goes,
And on one side the desert blows,
And with bell and voice and drum
Cities on the other hum;—
Where are forests, hot as fire,
Wide as England, tall as a spire,
Full of apes and cocoa-nuts
And the Negro hunters' huts;—
Where the knotty crocodile
Lies and blinks in the Nile,
And the red flamingo flies
Hunting fish before his eyes;—

There I'll come when I'm a man
With a camel caravan;
Light a fire in the gloom
Of some dusty dining-room;
See the pictures on the walls,
Heroes, fights, and festivals;
And in a corner find the toys
Of the old Egyptian boys.

THE ROAD TO RAFFYDIDDLE

MILDRED PLEW MEIGS

On the road to Raffydiddle
Sits a fiddler with a fiddle
   And there beneath the melting of the moon,
Each night he puts his chin
To his cheery violin
   And plucks him out a frisky feather tune.

And when as they go down
To Raffydiddle town
   The people hear him playing in the dusk,
Beside the crooked stile
They pause a little while
   To dance beneath the moon the moneymusk.

Oh, the fiddler he is slight
And his hair is salty white,
   And none who live will ever know his name.
But when he sets his bow
A tickle to and fro
   Each foot begins to flicker like a flame.

Oh, it's fun to see them come
When they hear the fiddle strum,
   All the lords and all the ladies with their cooks;
All the butchers and the bakers,
All the cake and candy makers,
   All the scholars with their noses in their books.

With their breeches in a crease,
Come the gorgeous blue police,
   Come the cowboys with their chaps upon their
     shins,
Comes a tailor spick-and-span
And a scissor-grinder man
   And a seamstress with her bosom full of pins.

Oh, it's fun to see them prance
At the Raffydiddle dance,

All the doctors and the judges in their gowns,
All the farmers in their slickers,
All the rag and bottle pickers,
   All the gypsies and the jockeys and the clowns.

There below the blinky stars
Come the tinkers and the tars,
   And the brigands with their daggers and their
     dirks,
Come the vixens and the villains
And the mammies with their "chilluns"
   And the chauffeurs and the soda water clerks.

On the road to Raffydiddle
Sits a fiddler with his fiddle,
   And round about the fiddler falls a cloak;
While past the crooked stile
In Raffydiddle file
   Come flitting all the merrymaking folk.

Oh, the fiddler he is old,
He is eery to behold,
   And none have guessed the riddle of his race;
But folk who linger long
To hear his final song
   Have often seen a sadness in his face.

On the road to Raffydiddle,
Sits a fiddler with his fiddle,
   And he fiddles and he fiddles in the dusk,
But those who come at dawn
Will find the fiddler gone
   And all the music melted into musk.

Every Raffydiddle tune
Will be shut up in the moon
   And none who seek will find his dark abode,
But where the music thinned
A creepy little wind
   Will ripple down the Raffydiddle road.

THE BEAR HUNT
MARGARET WIDDEMER

I played I was two polar bears
Who lived inside a cave of chairs,

And Brother was the hunter-man
Who tried to shoot us when we ran.

The ten-pins made good bones to gnaw,
I held them down beneath my paw.

Of course I had to kill him quick
Before he shot me with his stick,

So all the cave fell down, you see,
On Brother and the bones and me.

So then he said he wouldn't play—
But it was tea time anyway!

LITTLE ROBIN REDBREAST

Little Robin Redbreast
Sat upon a tree;
Up went Pussy-cat,
Down went he.

Down came Pussy-cat,
And away Robin ran;
Says little Robin Redbreast
"Catch me if you can."

Little Robin Redbreast
Hopped upon a wall;
Pussy-cat jumped after him,
And almost got a fall.

Little Robin chirped and sang,
And what did Pussy say?
Pussy-cat said "Mew,"
And Robin flew away.

OLD NURSERY RHYME

SELF-CONTROL
POLLY CHASE BOYDEN

My dolly would not play with me.
She simply stared
Her silly stare.
It made me *wild*
To pull her hair.

I kissed her *very quietly*
And walked outdoors and kicked a tree.

BOREDOM
MILDRED BOWERS ARMSTRONG

I can't blow bubbles,
I haven't any pipe.
I can't eat apples,
They haven't turned ripe.
If I sit quiet for an hour or two,
Will the Fairy Queen come to tell
  me what to do?

TWINKLE, TWINKLE, LITTLE STAR

Twinkle, twinkle, little star,
How I wonder what you are!
Up above the world so high,
Like a diamond in the sky.

When the blazing sun is gone,
When he nothing shines upon,
Then you show your little light,
Twinkle, twinkle, all the night.

Then the traveler in the dark
Thanks you for your tiny spark;
How could he see where to go,
If you did not twinkle so?

In the dark blue sky you keep,
Often through my curtains peep
For you never shut your eye,
Till the sun is in the sky.

As your bright and tiny spark
Lights the traveler in the dark,
Though I know not what you are,
Twinkle, twinkle, little star.
                              JANE TAYLOR

THE CHICKENS
ANONYMOUS

Said the first little chicken,
  With a queer little squirm,
"I wish I could find
  A fat little worm!"

Said the next little chicken,
  With an odd little shrug:
"I wish I could find
  A fat little bug!"

Said the third little chicken,
  With a small sigh of grief:
"I wish I could find
  A green little leaf!"

Said the fourth little chicken,
  With a faint little moan:
"I wish I could find
  A wee gravel stone!"

"Now see here!" said the mother,
  From the green garden patch,
"If you want any breakfast,
  Just come here and scratch!"

THERE WAS ONCE A PUFFIN

FLORENCE PAGE JAQUES

Oh, there once was a Puffin
Just the shape of a muffin,
And he lived on an island
In the
      bright
         blue sea!

He ate little fishes,
That were most delicious,
And he had them for supper
And he
     had
        them
            for tea.

But this poor little Puffin,
He couldn't play nothin',
For he hadn't anybody
To
    play
       with
          at all.

So he sat on his island,
And he cried for awhile, and
He felt very lonely,
And he
    felt
        very small.

Then along came the fishes,
And they said, "If you wishes,
You can have us for playmates,
Instead
    of
       for
         tea!"

So they now play together,
In all sorts of weather,
And the puffin eats pancakes,
Like you
    and
        like
           me.

MR. RABBIT

DIXIE WILLSON

Mr. Rabbit has a habit
That is very cute to see.

He wrinkles up and crinkles up
His little nose at me.

I like my little rabbit,
And I like his little brother,

And we have a lot of fun
Making faces at each other!